I ♥ LOVE YOU MORE THAN

Macaroni & Cheese

MISSY MITTEL PUBLISHING
E4637 Sunset View Lane
Weyauwega, WI 54983
www.missymittel.com

Ordering Information:
Quantity sales. Special discounts are available on quantity purchases by corporations, associations, and others. For details, contact the publisher at the address above.

Printed in the United States of America
ISBN: 978-0-578-42626-6

To my family and friends
who inspire love in my life every day.

A special thanks to my Paul,
who loves the silliness right out of me! This one is for you!

I love you so much ,

I can hardly BEAR it.

I love you more than macaroni and cheese.
The pickiest of eaters, it is certain to appease.

BUT, you are far more special than noodles and cheddar, just seeing your face always makes me feel better.

When the tree line is animated with colorful leaves,
your presence alone puts me at ease.

I love you more than Halloween, when we all go trick-or-treat.
Ghosts and goblins run wild like crazies in the street.

I love you more than the most vibrant sunset, gleaming in shades of purple, peach, and rosette.

When the sky is like a painting, a picture-perfect dream;
even equated with that, you still reign supreme.

They are definitely one of my most favorite treats,
but it can hardly come close to my love for YOU, Sweets.

I love you more than the first fallen snow,
how it glistens and glitters when it's fifteen below.

Snuggled in a blanket, watching flakes fall down;
you've got that beat just by being around.

I love you more than hot cocoa with marshmallows on top,
warming up after a day when the winds were nonstop.

Even compared to those first sweet sips,
I take more delight in a kiss from your lips.

I love you more than the first breezes of spring,
when the peepers start peeping, like a chorus they sing.

We open all of our windows to welcome the change,
but without you to celebrate, it would just feel mundane.

That feeling of anticipation that makes your heart race,
is always outdone when I'm in your embrace.

Even while splashing and acting like the fishes;
you're the sunshine in my days and the answer to my wishes.

I love you more than a warm summer night,
when you can see all the stars and the lightning bugs' light.

I love you more than all my favorite belongings.
I'd gladly give them up to keep you from my longings.

NOW, this universe is full of some wonderful stuff,
but my favorite things (times a million) could never be enough—

—for the moral of this story is plain and it's true,
there's just nothing out there that quite compares...

...to the love I feel
for you!

The End.

Don't forget to share the

LOVE.